Language! Readers

Level 1
Book A
Units 1–6

Jane Fell Greene
Judy Fell Woods

05   04   03   02   7   6   5   4

ISBN 1-57035-435-9
ISBN 1-57035-275-5 Set

Text layout and design by Kimberly Harris
Cover design by Becky Malone
Cover Image © 2000 by Digital Vision Ltd.
Illustrated by Peggy Ranson

This product is in compliance with AB2519 California State
Adoption revision requirements.

Printed in the United States of America

Published and Distributed by

SOPRIS
WEST

4093 Specialty Place • Longmont, CO 80504 • (303) 651-2829
www.sopriswest.com

Contents

SAM

UNIT 1

Phonology Concepts

- Spoken words are made of sounds (phonemes).
  - One speech sound is a phoneme.
  - Consonant sounds (phonemes) are closed sounds.
  - Consonant sound-symbol relationships:
    t, **s**, **m**, **b**, **c**, **f**
- Vowel sounds (phonemes) are open sounds.
  - Every word has a vowel phoneme.
  - Vowel sound-symbol relationship: short /a/

Vocabulary

a	cab	Sam
at	cat	Tab
Bam	fat	Tam
bat	mat	

SAM

Story Summary:

Sam's mom is calling him and his cat for dinner. Sam comes on his bike with the fat cat not far behind. They're both wet and dirty. Mom tells them to brush themselves off at the doormat before coming in. They're so dirty they have to beat the mud off the mat as well. They go in the house, slam the door behind them, and sit down to dinner.

"Sam! Sam!"

"Fat cat! Fat cat!"

Sam

A fat cat

Sam sat at a mat.

A fat cat sat at a mat.

Bat a mat,
Sam.

Bat a mat, fat
cat.

Bam! Bam!

Sam sat.

A fat cat sat.

Teacher/Parent Pages

Use the following questions to stimulate language growth, imagination, conceptual relationships, and higher-level thinking skills. These activities will encourage conversation and help develop language skills. Students must know that their ideas are important and that their questions will be heard. Have fun and accept all reasonable answers while praising and encouraging questioning from the students.

Vocabulary Expansion

Describe and define these words and phrases:

dusk	wheels	slam
appear	seat	doormat
dirty	ride	dinner
bike	spokes	brush
handlebars	pedals	beat

Language Expansion Activities

1. Draw a map of your neighborhood and tell about places where you can ride your bike.

2. Use clay to sculpt a bike you would like to own.

Language Expansion Questions

1. What were Sam and the cat doing in the story?

2. Why was Sam's mom calling them?

3. What did Sam and his cat have to do to themselves before they could go inside for dinner?

4. What happened to the door?

5. How did Sam and his cat feel at the beginning of the story? At the end of the story?

6. Was Sam's mom mad at him for being dirty?

7. Where do you think Sam and the fat cat had been?

8. Do you have a bike? Is it easy or hard to learn to ride? Why?

9. Tell about some places you would go if you could ride your bike anywhere.

10. Sam's mom was calling him to dinner. Does your mom or dad ever have to call you for dinner? What happens if your parent can't find you?

11. Have you ever been so dirty that your parent makes you brush yourself off at the doormat before he or she lets you in the house? Tell about it.

TAM

UNIT 1

Phonology Concepts

- Spoken words are made of sounds (phonemes).
  - One speech sound is a phoneme.
  - Consonant sounds (phonemes) are closed sounds.
  - Consonant sound-symbol relationships:
    t, **s**, **m**, **b**, **c**, **f**
- Vowel sounds (phonemes) are open sounds.
  - Every word has a vowel phoneme.
  - Vowel sound-symbol relationship: short /a/

Vocabulary

a	cab	Sam
at	cat	Tab
Bam	fat	Tam
bat	mat	

TAM

Story Summary:

Tam comes home from school and takes her dog, Tab, for a walk. Tab breaks his leash and runs after a cat. Tam calls Tab, but he keeps running away. Tam goes home, sits on her stoop, and cries. The cat runs into a garbage can to hide. Tab knocks down the can and the cat gets away. Tam calls Tab again and he finally comes home with his tail between his legs.

Tam

_____

Tab

_____

Tam sat at a
mat.

Tab, Tam

Tab at a cat!

"Tab! Tab!"

Tam sat at a mat.

Tab at a fat cat!

Bam! Bam!

"Tab! Tab!"

Tab sat at a mat.
Tam sat at a mat.

Teacher/Parent Pages

Use the following questions to stimulate language growth, imagination, conceptual relationships, and higher-level thinking skills. These activities will encourage conversation and help develop language skills. Students must know that their ideas are important and that their questions will be heard. Have fun and accept all reasonable answers while praising and encouraging questioning from the students.

Vocabulary Expansion

Describe and define these words and phrases:

school	steps	hide
walk	stroll	knock down
leash	garbage can	cry
dog	stoop	responsible
screen door	run away	tail

Language Expansion Activities

1. Make the noise Tab made when he knocked over the garbage can.

2. Draw pictures of your favorite pets.

Language Expansion Questions

1. What did Tam do when she got home from school?

2. What is Tam's dog's name?

3. What happened when Tab saw a cat?

4. Did Tab come the first time Tam called him?

5. Did Tab catch the cat?

6. What happened at the end of the story?

7. Do you think Tam is responsible for taking Tab for walks every day?

8. Why did Tab chase the cat?

9. Why did Tam put Tab on a leash?

10. What did Tam say to Tab when he finally got home?

11. Tam takes her dog for a walk after school. What do you do after school?

12. Many people have pets. Do all pets have to be taken care of?

13. Do you have a pet? What things do you have to do to take care of your pet?

AT BAT

UNIT 1

Phonology Concepts

- Spoken words are made of sounds (phonemes).
  - One speech sound is a phoneme.
  - Consonant sounds (phonemes) are closed sounds.
  - Consonant sound-symbol relationships:
    t, **s**, **m**, **b**, **c**, **f**
- Vowel sounds (phonemes) are open sounds.
  - Every word has a vowel phoneme.
  - Vowel sound-symbol relationship: short */a/*

Vocabulary

a	cab	Sam
at	cat	Tab
Bam	fat	Tam
bat	mat	

AT BAT

Story Summary:

Two children are at a baseball game anxiously waiting for their turn at bat. Both pals have good luck.

Sam sat.

Tam sat.

A fat cat sat.

A bat sat.

A fat mat sat.

Sam at a mat

Sam at bat

Bam!

Tam at a mat

Tam at bat

Bam!

Teacher/Parent Pages

Use the following questions to stimulate language growth, imagination, conceptual relationships, and higher-level thinking skills. These activities will encourage conversation and help develop language skills. Students must know that their ideas are important and that their questions will be heard. Have fun and accept all reasonable answers while praising and encouraging questioning from the students.

Vocabulary Expansion

Describe and define these words and phrases:

baseball	runs	three strikes
bull pen	home run	bases
coach	batter	out
dugout	umpire	inning
hits	pitcher	Little League
catcher		

Language Expansion Activities

1. Draw a picture of a baseball diamond. Why is it called a diamond? Look at your picture. Show where Sam and Tam were standing when they were at bat. Show where the umpire and the pitcher stand. Where do the people who watch the game sit?

2. Pretend that you and your friend are Sam and Tam. Play the game. Show how Sam and Tam felt when they won the game.

Language Expansion Questions

1. What were Sam and Tam doing in the story?

2. What happened after Sam and Tam stood on the mat?

3. What was the fat cat doing?

4. What happened when Sam and Tam were at bat?

5. How did Sam and Tam feel when they were sitting in the dugout waiting for the game to start?

6. Why are Sam and Tam dressed alike?

7. Why do some baseball players wear pads? masks?

8. What did the coach say to Sam and Tam after the game?

9. Did Tam and Sam feel happy after the game? How did the players on the other team feel?

10. Why do baseball players practice? Can you think of anybody else who has to practice? What do you practice?

11. Sometimes we win and sometimes we lose. How should we feel when we lose? Why?

12. Can you tell how to play a different game? (soccer, basketball, football, etc.) How are the games different? How are they alike?

13. Some people like to play ball. What other things do people do for fun?

AL

UNIT 2

Phonology Concepts

- A single unit of sound is a phoneme.
  - Consonant phonemes are closed sounds.
  - Consonant sound-symbol relationships:
    r, **h**, **j**, **l**, **p**, **n**
- Vowel phoneme concept: Every word has a vowel phoneme.
  - Vowel phonemes are open sounds.
  - Review: vowel sound-symbol relationship: short /a/
- Spoken words are made of phonemes.

Vocabulary

Al	has	man	pal	tan
as	hat	map	pat	
can	jab	nab	ran	
fan	jam	nap	rap	*the*
ham	lap	Nat	rat	

AL

Story Summary:

Sam is sitting alone, reading at a table in the library. At an adjoining table, Al sits reading books. Sam's fat cat jumps in through a window, just behind Al. He knocks over all the books, making lots of noise, and runs off. The librarian, who thinks Al is responsible for the ruckus, comes by and raps on the table. Sam runs after the cat and catches him. Sam and his fat cat make a new friend.

Al sat.

Sam sat.

The fat cat
ran.

Rap! Rap! Rap!

The fat cat
can jab Al.

Sam ran.

Sam can pat the
fat cat.

Al can pat the
cat.

A fat cat can
lap Al.

Sam has a pal.

Al has a pal.

Teacher/Parent Pages

Use the following questions to stimulate language growth, imagination, conceptual relationships, and higher-level thinking skills. These activities will encourage conversation and help develop language skills. Students must know that their ideas are important and that their questions will be heard. Have fun and accept all reasonable answers while praising and encouraging questioning from the students.

Vocabulary Expansion

Describe and define these words and phrases:

library	disturbance	borrow
librarian	sneak	library card
quiet	bookcases	friendly
books	carts	responsible
silent reading	check out	adjoining

Language Expansion Activities

1. Bring your favorite book to class. Tell your school friends about it.

2. Go to the library. Find a book that you think you will like. Find a book you think your pal will like.

Language Expansion Questions

1. What were Al and Sam doing when the story began?

2. How did the cat get into the library?

3. What did the cat do to cause a disturbance?

4. Sam chased his cat and picked him up. He lectured the fat cat and petted him at the same time. Sam wouldn't hurt his pet just because he made a mistake. Why is it always better to be kind to your pets, even if they misbehave? List three ways you can be kind to a pet.

5. What caused Sam and Al to be friends? Think of a time you made a new friend. Write about it.

6. Why was the librarian angry with Al? Do you think Sam was embarrassed? Have you ever been embarrassed? Tell about it.

7. Why is it important to be quiet in the library?

8. Why does the librarian try to keep the library quiet?

9. What kinds of books were Al and Sam reading? What kinds of books do you like to read?

10. People learn many things from books. What have you learned from books?

THE HAT

UNIT 2

Phonology Concepts

- A single unit of sound is a phoneme.
  - Consonant phonemes are closed sounds.
  - Consonant sound-symbol relationships: **r**, **h**, **j**, **l**, **p**, **n**
- Vowel phoneme concept: Every word has a vowel phoneme.
  - Vowel phonemes are open sounds.
  - Review: vowel sound-symbol relationship: short /a/
- Spoken words are made of phonemes.

Vocabulary

Al	has	man	pal	tan
as	hat	map	pat	
can	jab	nab	ran	
fan	jam	nap	rap	*the*
ham	lap	Nat	rat	

THE HAT

Story Summary:

Al's pal comes to play. He's wearing a large, tan sombrero. The boys fan themselves and play until they're worn out. They fall asleep with the big hat covering their faces. A man comes along, steals the hat, and runs away. Al gets the hat away from the man and gives it back to his pal.

Al has a pal.

The pal has a tan hat.

The hat can fan Al.

Al can fan the pal.

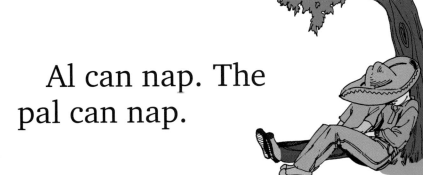

Al can nap. The pal can nap.

A man ran. The man can nab the tan hat.

The man has
the tan hat.

Al ran.

Al can nab
the tan hat.
The man ran.

Al has the tan hat.

The pal has
the tan hat.

Teacher/Parent Pages

Use the following questions to stimulate language growth, imagination, conceptual relationships, and higher-level thinking skills. These activities will encourage conversation and help develop language skills. Students must know that their ideas are important and that their questions will be heard. Have fun and accept all reasonable answers while praising and encouraging questioning from the students.

Vocabulary Expansion

Describe and define these words and phrases:

sombrero	doze	thief
best friend	grab	escape
steal	getaway	burglar
swipe	recover	
retrieve	chum	
classmate	catnap	

Language Expansion Activities

1. Dramatize the story using your pal's hat. Show how the pals felt when they woke up and found the hat missing.

2. Make paper hats with your chums. Decorate them any way you want. Decide what things you could do with the hats other than wear them.

Language Expansion Questions

1. Name the characters in the story.

2. What did the pal bring to Al's house?

3. What things did the pals do with the hat?

4. What happened after the boys fell asleep?

5. Do you think Al's pal was proud of his tan hat? What kind of hat was it?

6. Why did the man steal the hat?

7. What if Al hadn't recovered the hat? Create a new ending.

8. Do you think Al's pal will ever sleep outside again with his hat unprotected? Why?

9. If your pal lost his hat, would you try to retrieve it? What else could you do to try to get it back?

10. Judge what should happen to the man if he is caught.

11. Do you have a hat that you really love? Describe it.

12. People wear different hats for all different reasons. What are some reasons for wearing hats?

PAT

UNIT 2

Phonology Concepts

- A single unit of sound is a phoneme.
  - Consonant phonemes are closed sounds.
  - Consonant sound-symbol relationships:
    r, **h**, **j**, **l**, **p**, **n**
- Vowel phoneme concept: Every word has a vowel phoneme.
  - Vowel phonemes are open sounds.
  - Review: vowel sound-symbol relationship: short /a/
- Spoken words are made of phonemes.

Vocabulary

Al	has	man	pal	tan
as	hat	map	pat	
can	jab	nab	ran	
fan	jam	nap	rap	*the*
ham	lap	Nat	rat	

PAT

Story Summary:

Sam, Al, and Tam are walking down the sidewalk. Sam is carrying a gift basket. They stand at the doormat of the house of their new neighbor. After they each knock, Pat answers the door. She reaches down and pats Tam's dog, Tab. Sam gives Pat the basket, which contains homemade jams, and Al gives her a map of the neighborhood. The three friends have a new pal, and all four are happy.

Sam, Al,
Tam, Tab

At the mat

Sam can rap.
Al can rap. Tam
can rap.

Pat

Tab can lap
Pat. Pat can pat
Tab.

Al has the map.
Sam has the jam.

Pat has the map. Pat has the jam.

Al has a pal.

Sam has a pal.

Tam has a pal.

Pat as a
pal

Teacher/Parent Pages

Use the following questions to stimulate language growth, imagination, conceptual relationships, and higher-level thinking skills. These activities will encourage conversation and help develop language skills. Students must know that their ideas are important and that their questions will be heard. Have fun and accept all reasonable answers while praising and encouraging questioning from the students.

Vocabulary Expansion

Describe and define these words and phrases:

neighbors	surprise	basket
housewarming	lick	knock
gifts	new friend	homemade
greet	anticipate	welcome
plan	sidewalk	neighborhood

Language Expansion Activities

1. Tell your group about the best gift you have ever received. Paint a picture of it.

2. Draw a map of your neighborhood and show it to your parents and some of your neighbors.

Language Expansion Questions

1. Why were the pals walking down the street?

2. What did they do when they got to the door?

3. What happened after they knocked on the door?

4. Was Pat glad to see the friends?

5. Do you think Pat liked Tab? Why?

6. Why do you think the pals brought a map for the new neighbors? homemade jam?

7. How did Pat feel when she saw the pals?

8. Have you ever moved to a new neighborhood? Is it easy to make new friends?

9. Has a new family ever moved into your neighborhood? What did you do to make them feel welcome?

10. Why do people give each other gifts?

11. When you do something nice for someone else, your actions can be gifts. What actions can you give your parents as gifts?

12. Why is it a good idea for all of the people in a neighborhood to know each other and be friends?

THE MAN

UNIT 3

Phonology Concepts

- A single unit of sound is a phoneme.
    - Consonant phonemes are closed sounds.
    - Consonant sound-symbol relationships: **d̲**, **g**, **v̲**
- Vowel phoneme concept: Every word has a vowel phoneme.
    - Vowel phonemes are open sounds.
    - Review: vowel sound-symbol relationship: short /a/
- Spoken words are made of phonemes.

Vocabulary

bad	gal	lag	rag	vat
bag	gas	lap	sad	
ban	had	mad	sag	*do*
dad	lab	pad	tag	*to*
dam	lad	Pam	van	

THE MAN

Story Summary:

Pat and Sam are in karate class. They stretch on mats and run laps around the gym. Suddenly, they start chasing each other, not paying attention to the teacher. He stops them and brings them back to the class. They jab the punching bag. When class is over, both children are tired and sit down on the mats to rest.

The man sat at a mat.

Pat sat at a mat. Sam sat at a mat.

The man ran a lap.

Sam ran a lap.
Pat ran a lap.

Sam ran to Pat.

Can Sam tag
Pat? Can Pat
tag Sam?

The man can
nab Sam. The man
can nab Pat.

The man can
jab the bag.

Pat can jab the
bag.

Sam can jab
the bag.

Pat can sag!
Sam can sag!

Teacher/Parent Pages

Use the following questions to stimulate language growth, imagination, conceptual relationships, and higher-level thinking skills. These activities will encourage conversation and help develop language skills. Students must know that their ideas are important and that their questions will be heard. Have fun and accept all reasonable answers while praising and encouraging questioning from the students.

Vocabulary Expansion

Describe and define these words and phrases:

karate	punch	fidgeting
weapons	punching bag	listening
training	exercise	instructor
practice	mats	
kick	rules	
self-defense	black belt	

Language Expansion Activities

1. Imagine how a karate class looks. Create a picture of how you think it looks. Where does the instructor stand? Where do the students stand? Where are the punching bags?

2. Dramatize the story with your friends from school or from your neighborhood.

Language Expansion Questions

1. Tell who the man is.

2. Why did Pat and Sam do stretching exercises on a mat?

3. Tell about three things Pat and Sam did in karate class.

4. Why did the instructor grab Sam and Pat?

5. Why did the children feel tired when class was over?

6. What other things could Pat and Sam have done in karate class? Do you take any lessons? What kinds of things do you do in your lessons?

7. Imagine what you would do if you had earned a black belt in karate.

8. What are some things a karate instructor does during the day?

9. Imagine that Pat and Sam are at a karate match. Create a new ending for the story.

10. Decide whether or not karate is a good sport. Explain your answer.

11. Pat and Sam were not listening and got in trouble with their instructor. What happens when you don't listen to your teachers or parents?

THE VAN

UNIT 3

Phonology Concepts

- A single unit of sound is a phoneme.
  - Consonant phonemes are closed sounds.
  - Consonant sound-symbol relationships:
    d, **g**, **v**
- Vowel phoneme concept: Every word has a vowel phoneme.
  - Vowel phonemes are open sounds.
  - Review: vowel sound-symbol relationship: short /a/
- Spoken words are made of phonemes.

Vocabulary

bad	gal	lag	rag	vat
bag	gas	lap	sad	
ban	had	mad	sag	*do*
dad	lab	pad	tag	*to*
dam	lad	Pam	van	

72

THE VAN

Story Summary:

On a lonely highway a father and his son wait beside their broken-down van. Dad tries to repair it. The boy naps on the grass. Dad has no luck fixing the van. He loses his temper and begins to "rap, jab, and bam" the van. It refuses to start. A cab comes by and gives them a ride.

Dad had a
bad van.

Dad had a sad
lad.

The sad lad
had to nap.

The bad
van had gas.

Dad had to
pat the bad
van.

Mad Dad had to rap the
bad van. Mad Dad had to jab
the bad van. Mad Dad had to
bam the bad van.

The bad van
had to sag.
The bad van
had to lag.

A fat man had
a cab.

The cab
had gas.

Do Dad and the sad lad ban the van? Dad and the lad do ban the van.

The cab had the fat man, mad Dad, and the sad lad.

Teacher/Parent Pages

Use the following questions to stimulate language growth, imagination, conceptual relationships, and higher-level thinking skills. These activities will encourage conversation and help develop language skills. Students must know that their ideas are important and that their questions will be heard. Have fun and accept all reasonable answers while praising and encouraging questioning from the students.

Vocabulary Expansion

Describe and define these words and phrases:

highway	hood	wrench
broken	motor	screwdriver
repair	vehicle	taxi
gentle	tools	rescue
temper	fuel	abandon

Language Expansion Activities

1. Use puppets and pretend they are fixing a van. What tools would they need? Can they fix the van?

2. Along with your pals, try to make the noises vans and cars make when they break down. Reward the pal who makes the best noises.

Language Expansion Questions

1. Why were Dad and his son standing by a lonely highway?

2. What did Dad do to try to repair the van?

3. What did the lad do while Dad was trying to repair the vehicle?

4. What happens to Dad's temper when he can't fix the van?

5. What happens in the end?

6. How would the story be different if Dad fixed the van?

7. Could the events in this story really happen? Has anything like this ever happened to you?

8. Compare the lad's dad to your own dad. How are they alike? How are they different?

9. People often get angry when they can't solve a problem. What do you do when you can't solve a problem? Can you think of something Dad could have done differently in the story?

10. Dad and the lad had to abandon their van. Did you ever have to leave something behind because it was broken or didn't work anymore? Tell about it.

11. The cab driver rescued Dad and the lad. Have you or anyone you know ever been rescued? Explain what happened.

Unit 3, Book 3

THE BAD CAT

UNIT 3

Phonology Concepts

- A single unit of sound is a phoneme.
  - Consonant phonemes are closed sounds.
  - Consonant sound-symbol relationships:
    d̲, **g**, **v̲**
- Vowel phoneme concept: Every word has a vowel phoneme.
  - Vowel phonemes are open sounds.
  - Review: vowel sound-symbol relationship: short /a/
- Spoken words are made of phonemes.

Vocabulary

bad	gal	lag	rag	vat
bag	gas	lap	sad	
ban	had	mad	sag	*do*
dad	lab	pad	tag	*to*
dam	lad	Pam	van	

THE BAD CAT

Story Summary:

The cab from the preceding story, carrying Dad and his lad, pulls up to a highway cafe to get gas. Inside, Pam, a waitress, is cleaning the counters with a rag. She places food (ham and jam) on the counter. A plump cat gets inside and jumps on the counter and takes the rag. The cat knocks the jam over onto the lad, then jumps onto the nearby table and knocks the whole ham onto Dad. Pam, disgusted, sits down. The driver calls for Dad and the lad to come with him after he fills his cab with gas. They leave.

A dad, a lad, a man

Pam had a rag.

Pam had the ham. Pam had the jam.

Pam had a bad cat. The cat ran.

The bad cat had the rag.

The sad lad had the jam. The mad dad had the ham.

The bad cat sat.

Pam had the rag.

Pam had the ham. Pam had the jam.

The cab had gas.

The cab ran. The cab had Dad. The cab had the lad.

Teacher/Parent Pages

Use the following questions to stimulate language growth, imagination, conceptual relationships, and higher-level thinking skills. These activities will encourage conversation and help develop language skills. Students must know that their ideas are important and that their questions will be heard. Have fun and accept all reasonable answers while praising and encouraging questioning from the students.

Vocabulary Expansion

Describe and define these words and phrases:

cafe	cleaning	disgusted
highway	counters	fill up
gas pump	hungry	speed
inside	lunch	travel
waitress	driver	journey

Language Expansion Activities

1. Pretend you own a restaurant. Have your friends be waiters and waitresses. Let your teachers or parents be the customers.

2. Make a gas pump out of clay. Use matchbox cars or small boxes painted to look like cars. Play "fill 'er up."

Language Expansion Questions

1. Why did the cab driver have to stop at the highway cafe?

2. What did Dad and his son do while the cab driver was filling up his cab with gas?

3. Describe what happened after the father and son got their food.

4. Do you think Pam was a good waitress? Explain your answer.

5. What do you think happened to the cat?

6. What happened at the end of the story?

7. Dad and the lad ordered food at the cafe, but they didn't get to eat anything because of the bad cat. Do you think they had to pay for the food? Tell why or why not.

8. Have you ever eaten at a cafe or restaurant? Recall what it was like. What was your favorite food served to you?

9. Sometimes our pets do not behave apppropriately. Do you have a pet who has gotten into trouble? Tell about it.

10. It's not easy to own a restaurant. What are some of the problems people have who own restaurants? What are some good reasons to own a restaurant?

11. The cab driver in this story had to stop because his cab was running out of fuel. Did you ever ride in a car that ran out of gas? Tell that story.

A BIG B

UNIT 4

Phonology Concepts

- A single unit of sound is a phoneme.
  - Consonant phonemes are closed sounds.
  - Consonant sound-symbol relationship:
    w
- Vowel phoneme concept: Every word has a vowel phoneme.
  - Vowel phonemes are open sounds.
  - Vowel sound-symbol relationship: short /i/
- Spoken words are made of phonemes.

Vocabulary

bit	in	pig	win	*have*
did	is	rig	wit	*I*
him	it	rim		*video*
his	kid	sit		
hit	lid	tin		

A BIG B

Story Summary:

Al's dad takes Al and Sam to a fast food store. They order Big B hamburgers. Just as they begin to eat their sandwiches, Sam's fat cat grabs them and knocks the Big Bs on the floor. The boys run back into the restaurant and the waitress gives them another order. Back in the car again, Sam begins to bite into the sandwich when the fat cat jumps up and takes a bite! Al thinks it's funny and teases Sam. Sam is mad at his pet. The fat cat grins and eats the rest of Sam's Big B.

Al sat in the van. Sam sat in the van. Dad sat in the van.

"Can I have a Big B?"
"Can I have a Big B?"

Al had the bag. Sam had his fat cat. The fat cat hit the bag. Bam! The bag had a rip.

In ran Sam. In ran Al. "The bag has a big rip!"

The gal had a Big B. The Big B had a lid. Sam had it.

In the van, Al bit in to his Big B. "Dad, I have a Big B. Sam has his Big B. Have a Big B, Dad!"

Sam bit in to his Big B. The fat cat bit in to the Big B.

Sam is mad. His Big B is in his lap.

"Fat cat did it. Bad cat!"

"Sam! The fat cat is a pig! Did the fat cat have a Big B?"

"I am mad. I have had it. The fat cat had the Big B. The fat cat is as fat as a pig."

The fat cat sat.

Teacher/Parent Pages

Use the following questions to stimulate language growth, imagination, conceptual relationships, and higher-level thinking skills. These activities will encourage conversation and help develop language skills. Students must know that their ideas are important and that their questions will be heard. Have fun and accept all reasonable answers while praising and encouraging questioning from the students.

Vocabulary Expansion

Describe and define these words and phrases:

fast food	sandwich	enjoy
pet	funny	meal
waiter	disgusted	breakfast
place an order	hungry	lunch
drive-through	tease	dinner

Language Expansion Activities

1. Draw a picture of the things you would like to order at a drive-through window. Write the name of each thing under its picture.

2. Make a list of all of the places you can go to order from a drive-through window. Compare your list with others from your classmates. Make a big list from everybody's small lists.

Language Expansion Questions

1. What did Sam and Al order when they went to the drive-through window?

2. What happened after they got their order from the drive-through window?

3. When Sam and Al had to go inside to order another hamburger, how did Sam feel? How did Al feel?

4. When the boys got back into the van and got ready to eat, what happened? What do you think Al really meant when he said, "The fat cat is a pig"?

5. Sam loved his pet, the fat cat. But on the day of this story, can you explain how Sam was feeling about his pet? Is it possible to love someone one day, but feel angry with them on another day?

6. Why do you think people enjoy having pets?

7. If Sam was mad about what happened, why did Al think it was so funny? How do you feel when you're angry about something and somebody else laughs? Can you think of a time that you laughed when your friend was mad?

8. The bad cat spilled food in his van, but Al's dad was not mad. Why do you think Al's dad was laughing?

9. What should you do if you or your pet damages something that belongs to someone else?

10. When you're feeling unhappy, what can you do to make yourself feel better? Is it a good thing to sit and pout? Why?

Unit 4, Book 2

I AM SIS

UNIT 4

Phonology Concepts

- A single unit of sound is a phoneme.
    - Consonant phonemes are closed sounds.
    - Consonant sound-symbol relationship:
      <u>**w**</u>
- Vowel phoneme concept: Every word has a vowel phoneme.
    - Vowel phonemes are open sounds.
    - Vowel sound-symbol relationship: short /i/
- Spoken words are made of phonemes.

Vocabulary

bit	in	pig	win	*have*
did	is	rig	wit	*I*
him	it	rim		*video*
his	kid	sit		
hit	lid	tin		

I AM SIS

Story Summary:

Sis is daydreaming about things she wishes she could do. She is dreaming about hitting a home run over the fence at the ballpark. She is imagining buying a pig at an auction and maybe becoming a farmer. She is fantasizing about being a heroine and saving her town from flooding. She is even daydreaming about being a sheriff. Sis is also dreaming of beating her dad in a game of tag and of becoming a rap star. Sis is having big dreams—and she knows she can become anything she wants. Sis can do it!

I am Sis.

I have a bat. I have a mit. I can hit. I hit it to the rim. Bam! I hit it to the rim!

I can win a big pig. I can bid: 2 – 4 – 6 – 8 – 10. 10 can win! I can win the pig!

I can ram in to a dam. I can do it. I can fix a dam!

I can tag the man. The man has a tin tag. Can the man tag Sis?

I can tag Dad. I can tag the van. I can do it. Can Dad tag Sis?

I can hit it to the rim! I can bid to have a pig. I can fix a dam. I can tag Dad.

I am hip. I can do it! I can do it!

I am hip. I can rap.

Am I hip? I am! Can I win? I can!

Can I do it? I can. I am Sis!

Teacher/Parent Pages

Use the following questions to stimulate language growth, imagination, conceptual relationships, and higher-level thinking skills. These activities will encourage conversation and help develop language skills. Students must know that their ideas are important and that their questions will be heard. Have fun and accept all reasonable answers while praising and encouraging questioning from the students.

Vocabulary Expansion

Describe and define these words and phrases:

kidding	actor	female
auction	pretend	play
costume	rap	fantasy
daydream	sheriff	auctioneer
reality	tall tales	dam

Language Expansion Activities

1. Let one person in your class be Sis. Others can be the pig, the dam, the man, and the dad. Act out the story. Then take turns being Sis doing other funny things.

2. Have a mock auction in the classroom. Bid on each student's favorite classroom or shared item. Take turns being the auctioneer.

Language Expansion Questions

1. What happened when Sis dreamed of hitting the ball over the fence? Do you think that's something that could ever happen for Sis? Why?

2. How do you know that the man in the tin tag is the sheriff? What does a sheriff do?

3. Do you think it's fair to say that Sis is not able to pass her dad and tag him at the age of 6? Why do parents sometimes let their kids win? Do you think this is OK?

4. Sis says, "I am hip. I can rap." What does that mean? What is the difference between talking and rapping?

5. How does Sis feel at the end of the story? What is self-esteem? Why is it a good thing to have positive self-esteem? How can you get it if you don't have it?

6. Do you think it's OK to daydream about doing silly things? Do you ever daydream? What kinds of things do you daydream about?

7. When people talk about kidding each other, what does that mean? Do you ever kid your mom or your dad? Do you ever kid anybody else? Does anybody ever kid you?

8. Is kidding OK? Should someone be punished for kidding? If kidding hurts another person, then is it still OK?

9. When someone makes up a long story, sometimes the story becomes a play. What does it take to make a story a play? Can a play become a television program? What television programs do you like?

10. "Hip" and "rap" are words that aren't usually used in school. Why?

AL AND HIS VIDEO PAD

UNIT 4

Phonology Concepts

- A single unit of sound is a phoneme.
  - Consonant phonemes are closed sounds.
  - Consonant sound-symbol relationship:
    w
- Vowel phoneme concept: Every word has a vowel phoneme.
  - Vowel phonemes are open sounds.
  - Vowel sound-symbol relationship: short /i/
- Spoken words are made of phonemes.

Vocabulary

bit	in	pig	win	*have*
did	is	rig	wit	*I*
him	it	rim		*video*
his	kid	sit		
hit	lid	tin		

AL AND HIS VIDEO PAD

Story Summary:

Al has a video game with a power pad. In the game he is playing, it is hard to beat the tan kid. To win, Al has to run fast on the power pad. After he keeps trying many times, he wins.

Al has a video.

It is his video.

Al has a big pad at the video. Al can rig the pad to the video.

Can Al lap
to win at his
video pad?

Al can hit the
pad. Can Al have
wit? Can Al win?

A tan kid is in
the video. The
tan kid has wit.

The tan kid can lap. Can the tan kid lag? Can Al tag the tan kid? Al can lap.

Al can tag the tan kid to have a win.

The kid in the video is sad.

Did Al win at
the video pad?

It is his big
win!

Teacher/Parent Pages

Use the following questions to stimulate language growth, imagination, conceptual relationships, and higher-level thinking skills. These activities will encourage conversation and help develop language skills. Students must know that their ideas are important and that their questions will be heard. Have fun and accept all reasonable answers while praising and encouraging questioning from the students.

Vocabulary Expansion

Describe and define these words and phrases:

video games	outsmart	determination
screen	power pad	difficult
monitor	cartridge	remote control
technology	clever	wit
run a lap	joystick	celebrate

Language Expansion Activities

1. Pretend you are at the power pad. Run in place with your friend and have another pal decide who the winner is. Write a story about your game.

2. Make your own power pad from paper and crayons. Explain to your friends how it would work if it were the real one.

Language Expansion Questions

1. What special feature did Al have for his video game?

2. At the beginning of the game, Al was trying to beat someone on the video screen. Who was it?

3. Was the tan kid faster than Al at the beginning of the game?

4. What did Al have to do to beat the tan kid?

5. Do you think that Al really wanted to win the game? Why do you think so?

6. Do you think that the tan kid had ever beaten Al before? Is it easy to win video games?

7. Have you ever played on a power pad? Have you ever seen one on TV?

8. Do you know the names of other video games? Which ones do you know about?

9. Some kids don't like video games. If you don't like them, what do you like to do for fun?

10. Some kids play video games at a mall instead of at home. Have you ever been to a mall where there are video games? Some kids get mad at the video games. Is that a smart thing to do? Why?

THE BACK PACK

UNIT 5

Phonology Concepts

- A single unit of sound is a phoneme.
  - Consonant phonemes are closed sounds.
  - Consonant sound-symbol relationships:
    k, **ck**
  - Vowels are open sounds (phonemes).
  - Review: vowel sound-symbol relationships: short /a/, short /i/

Vocabulary

back	pack	sick	*said*
hack	pick	tack	
kick	rack		
Mac	sack		

THE BACK PACK

Story Summary:

The friends are walking home from school when they meet a new kid, Mat. They talk to Mat and make friends walking home. Mat's having a hard time carrying his books and papers because he doesn't have a back pack. When they get to Pat's house, Pat's dad gives Mat an old back pack from his garage. Mat is very pleased and thanks Pat's dad.

Pat has a back pack. Kim has a back pack.

Sam has a back pack. Al has a back pack.

Can the kid in the cap have a back pack?

The big kid in the cap is a sad lad. The big kid in the cap is Mat.

Mat said, "Sam has a big back pack. Al has a big back pack. Can I have a back pack?"

Sam sat. Kim sat. Pat sat. Al sat.

"Dad! Dad!" said Pat. "The big kid is Mat."

"Can Mat have the back pack?"

"Have it," said Dad. "Have the back pack, Mat."

Pat said, "Have the back pack, Mat. Dad had a back pack."

Mat said, "It is a back pack! I have a big back pack."

Teacher/Parent Pages

Use the following questions to stimulate language growth, imagination, conceptual relationships, and higher-level thinking skills. These activities will encourage conversation and help develop language skills. Students must know that their ideas are important and that their questions will be heard. Have fun and accept all reasonable answers while praising and encouraging questioning from the students.

Vocabulary Expansion

Describe and define these words and phrases:

student	stoplight	grateful
homework	garage	approach
huge	cautious	generous
sidewalk	street	organize
overloaded	driveway	traffic

Language Expansion Activities

1. Write a list of the names of all of your friends. Beside each name, list a special gift you'd like to give your friend.

2. In small groups of two or three, write special directions for being cautious when walking. Think about things like street corners, traffic, and strangers.

Language Expansion Questions

1. How were the kids carrying their books home?

2. Why are Pat, Kim, Sam, and Al carrying books home from school?

3. Why is it so hard for Mat to carry all of his books?

4. Why do you think the kids were afraid of Mat? Should we be afraid of people just because they're big?

5. How did Mat feel when he first met the other four kids?

6. When Pat's dad drove up, what did he do for Mat?

7. Where do you think Pat's dad had been?

8. What do you think Mat did after he got his back pack?

9. Has a new friend of yours ever needed anything? Were you able to help? How?

10. Not everybody walks home from school. What other ways do students get home? How do you go home from school in the afternoon? How would you like to go home?

A KID
CAN WIN

UNIT 5

Phonology Concepts

- A single unit of sound is a phoneme.
    - Consonant phonemes are closed sounds.
    - Consonant sound-symbol relationships:
      k, **ck**
    - Vowels are open sounds (phonemes).
    - Review: vowel sound-symbol relationships: short /a/, short /i/

Vocabulary

back	pack	sick	*said*
hack	pick	tack	
kick	rack		
Mac	sack		

A KID CAN WIN

Story Summary:

Pat and Kim are in Kim's backyard, picking weeds out of her mother's garden. Tam comes in the back gate with her little sister, Sis. Tam has to baby-sit for Sis this afternoon because Sis had a temper tantrum at home and Dad didn't want her to disturb the twins' nap. Tam, Pat, and Kim play tag. Tam makes Sis sit down while the older girls play. Kim is the fastest runner, and Pat and Tam are unable to catch her. Finally Sis announces that she can tag Kim. Tam tells her to sit down and be quiet, but Sis gets up, runs after Kim, and tags her. The big girls are not happy when little Sis outruns them.

Kim is in the back. Pat is in the back. Kim can pick. Pat can pick.

"Kim! Kim!" Tam said.
Tam is in the back. Sis is in the back.

"I have Sis," Tam said. "Dad is mad at Sis. Sis had a fit. Dad said I had to have Sis."

134

Tam is mad. Sis is sad.

"Do I have to have Sis?" Tam said. Tam is mad. "Sit, Sis. Sit." Tam said.

Pat ran. "Tag Kim," said Tam. Pat ran back to Tam.

"Tag Kim," said Pat, "Do it, Tam. Tag Kim." Kim ran a lap. Tam ran back to Pat.

Can Pat tag
Kim? Can Tam
tag Kim? Pat ran
back. Tam ran
back.

Sis said, "I can! I
can tag Kim!"
Tam said, "Sit,
Sis! Sit!"

Pat said, "Tam, can
Sis tag Kim?"
"I am mad at Sis.
Sis had a fit. Sit,
Sis, sit!" said Tam.

"Can Sis do it?" said Pat.

Sis ran to tag Kim. Sis ran! Sis can tag Kim! Sis said, "I ran to Kim. I had to! I can tag Kim! I ran to win."

Pat sat. Tam sat. Kim sat.

"Sis can do it. Sis can tag Kim," Pat said. "A kid can win!" said Tam.

Teacher/Parent Pages

Use the following questions to stimulate language growth, imagination, conceptual relationships, and higher-level thinking skills. These activities will encourage conversation and help develop language skills. Students must know that their ideas are important and that their questions will be heard. Have fun and accept all reasonable answers while praising and encouraging questioning from the students.

Vocabulary Expansion

Describe and define these words and phrases:

backyard	outside	outdoor games
tag	garden	sister
in charge	taking care of	baby-sitting
racing	chasing	afternoon
responsible	catch	fastest

Language Expansion Activities

1. Play a game of tag with your friends at school or in your neighborhood. Which pals are the fastest? Tell your parents about who the fastest runners are.

2. Draw a picture of your family. Do you have any sisters or brothers? Write their names under their pictures. Tell about the people in your family.

Language Expansion Questions

1. What were Pat and Kim doing in the backyard at the beginning of the story?

2. Who came to play with them?

3. Why did Tam have to bring her little sister with her? Was she happy about it?

4. What game did the big girls play while Sis sat in the yard?

5. How do you think Sis felt while the girls were playing and she had to sit and be quiet?

6. Why did Sis finally decide to join in the game, even after her big sister had told her to sit down?

7. How did the big girls feel when Sis won the game of tag?

8. When you play outdoor games with your friends, are there any young children in your neighborhood who are good at outdoor games? How does it feel when a younger child beats you at a game?

9. Remember: Everybody is not good at everything, but we should try our best and have fun. What things are you good at? What things are you not so good at? Can you lose a game and still have fun? Why?

10. Tam and her little sister were not happy with each other that day. Sometimes, sisters and brothers fight, but other days they have fun. Why do you think brothers and sisters have so many arguments?

AL IS HIT

UNIT 5

Phonology Concepts

- A single unit of sound is a phoneme.
    - Consonant phonemes are closed sounds.
    - Consonant sound-symbol relationships: **k**, **ck**
    - Vowels are open sounds (phonemes).
    - Review: vowel sound-symbol relationships: short $/a/$, short $/i/$

Vocabulary

back	pack	sick	*said*
hack	pick	tack	
kick	rack		
Mac	sack		

AL IS HIT

Story Summary:

Dad and the pals are in the backyard playing baseball. Sam hits a pop fly right to Al, but Al's glove has a tack in it, and when the ball hits his glove, Al gets hurt, runs backward into the street, and accidentally is hit by a cab. Dad and the pals get a stretcher and take Al to the hospital. A nurse checks him in, and he lies on the stretcher, unconscious. The cab driver, the children, and Dad all wonder what will happen to Al.

Sam is in the back, at bat. Dad is in back.

Al has a tan mitt.

Tam is at the pad.

Pat said, "Hit it, Sam! Hit it! Win!"

Sam can pick a bat.
Sam hit it. Bam! Al
ran back to have it.
A tack is in his mitt.
Al can sag.

"A cab! A cab!"
said Tam.

"Did the big cab hit Al? Is Al hit?" said Sam.

"Al is hit," said the hack man. "I hit him in the back." The hack man is sad.

Dad ran to the tan van. "Get a mat on a rack to Al! Pack him in back!" said Dad.

Al is sick. His hip is bad. His back is bad.

The gal has a pad. "Tag the lad," said the gal. "Did a cab hit Al?"

Al can nap in the mat. Tam is sad. Sam is sad. Pat is mad at the hack man. The hack man is sad. Dad is at the mat.

Teacher/Parent Pages

Use the following questions to stimulate language growth, imagination, conceptual relationships, and higher-level thinking skills. These activities will encourage conversation and help develop language skills. Students must know that their ideas are important and that their questions will be heard. Have fun and accept all reasonable answers while praising and encouraging questioning from the students.

Vocabulary Expansion

Describe and define these words and phrases:

baseball	glove	popfly
obstacle	accident	victim
hack	injury	dart
hospital	stretcher	nurse
unconscious	grieve	wonder

Language Expansion Activities

1. Ask your parents or teacher to take you to your local hospital. Sometimes hospitals give tours to students. See if your hospital will take you on a tour. Predict what things you will see there.

2. Write a story about a hospital trip or an accident or illness of someone who went to the hospital. Share it with your pals.

Language Expansion Questions

1. What game were the pals playing?

2. Who was at bat in the beginning of the story?

3. What happened when Al tried to catch the ball?

4. What did Dad tell the children to do?

5. How did the cab driver feel when he saw Al dart into the street in front of him?

6. Was the cab driver at fault? Why?

7. Dad knew he could move Al without further injuring him. If Dad hadn't been there to help the children with Al, what should they have done?

8. Accidents happen every day. When children are playing alone and someone is injured, what emergency phone number should they call? Should someone stay with the victim? Why?

9. Have you ever been to a hospital? What kinds of people work in hospitals? What equipment is used in hospitals?

10. Hospitals are places where people are helped. What other places can you think of that help people?

Unit 6, Book 1

TO A SICK KID

UNIT 6

Phonology Concepts

- Place value for encoding: **-ck** (represents /k/ at the end of one-syllable words)
- Sometimes spelling depends on whether a sound comes at the beginning, middle, or end of a word.
- When the /k/ sound comes at the end of a one-syllable word, the spelling is almost always **-ck.**
  - Exception: when Mac is an abbreviated name (**Macmillan**, **Macarthur**)

Vocabulary

back	Nick	Rick	*of*
kick	pack	sack	
Mack	pick	sick	
Mick	Rat Pack	tack	

To A Sick Kid

Story Summary:

Sam and Tam are sad because their friend, Al, is in the hospital. They decide to write letters to Al and tell him things that have been happening in the neighborhood since his accident. They pack the letters into the rig attached to the back of Sam's bicycle and take the letters to Al themselves.

Al is sick. His
back is bad.
His hip is bad.

Sam is sad.
Tam is sad.

"Can I have a
pad, Tam?" said
Sam.

"I have a pad. It is at the back of the sack," said Tam.

"Sit, Tam. Al is a sick kid. Sit and rap to him."

Sam can rap to Al. Sam said his cat is sick. Sam said his back pack is sad. It has a big rip in it.

Tam can rap to Al. Tam said the tack in the mitt is big. Tam said the tip of his mitt has a rip.

Sam said his rig had a tin rack. The cat fits in to the rack. The fat cat had a nap in the rack of the rig.

"At Kim's," Tam said to Al, "Sis ran to tag Kim." Tam said, "Al, a kid can win!"

Tam has a bit of jam in a big tin can. "Dan said to fit the jam tin in the back pack," said Tam. "I can pack it to Al."

"Tam," said Sam, "Can I fit the pad in the back pack? I can fit the back pack in the rack of the rig. Al can have the pad. The tin of jam is his."

Teacher/Parent Pages

Use the following questions to stimulate language growth, imagination, conceptual relationships, and higher-level thinking skills. These activities will encourage conversation and help develop language skills. Students must know that their ideas are important and that their questions will be heard. Have fun and accept all reasonable answers while praising and encouraging questioning from the students.

Vocabulary Expansion

Describe and define these words and phrases:

sympathy	letter	ill
hospital	stationery	remembering
accident	gratifying	write
bicycle rig	get well note	stamp
address	return address	envelope

Language Expansion Activities

1. Write a letter to someone. Whom will you write? What will you write?

2. Think of things you could do for people who are sick. Make a list of these things. Do some of them. Explain why helping sick people is gratifying.

Language Expansion Questions

1. Who was hurt? What was wrong with him?

2. Why were Sam and Tam sad?

3. What did the pals decide to do for Al?

4. What were two things friends said had happened while Al was in the hospital? Can you think of all the things that Sam and Tam wrote to Al? Look back at the story to help you remember.

5. How did Sam and Tam feel after they wrote Al their letters?

6. Al has been hurt. How will the letters help Al to feel better?

7. It is a good idea to write letters to people in the hospital. Who else would feel good if you wrote them a letter?

8. When people have been in serious accidents, why is it better for them to be in the hospital than at home?

9. What happens to people who are in the hospital if nobody writes them letters or goes to see them?

10. Why is it all right to be near someone who has a broken bone, but a good idea to stay away from someone who has the flu?

Unit 6, Book 2

A BIT OF
A NAP

UNIT 6

Phonology Concepts

- Place value for encoding: **-ck** (represents /k/ at the end of one-syllable words)
- Sometimes spelling depends on whether a sound comes at the beginning, middle, or end of a word.
- When the /k/ sound comes at the end of a one-syllable word, the spelling is almost always **-ck.**
  - Exception: when Mac is an abbreviated name (**Macmillan**, **Macarthur**)

Vocabulary

back	Nick	Rick	*of*
kick	pack	sack	
Mack	pick	sick	
Mick	Rat Pack	tack	

A BIT OF A NAP

Story Summary:

Al was hit by a cab and is in the hospital. Al's parents come to visit him every day. Al is getting better and today Al gets to go home. His dad comes to pick him up. The nurse reminds Al that he has to keep taking his medicine, gives Al a hug, and says good-bye. Al and his dad head home.

Al said to his dad, "Dad, the gal said I have to have a bit of a nap."

"Do I have to nap, Dad?" said Al. Dad said Al had to nap. "Can you nap, Dad?" said Al. "Can you hit the sack?"

"I can sit, Al," said Dad. "If you can nap, I can sit."

Dad has Al's back pack in his lap. Dad can pack his bag. Dad can fit a tin of jam in his back pack.

Al can tap his lip. "Dad, did you have a bit of a nap?" said Al.

"I can pack the bag," said Dad. "You have the nap."

Al has his nap. Dad can sit. Dad has a cat nap.

"Sit, Al," said the gal. "You have to sip it to the rim."

"It is bad to sip," said Al. "Do I have to?"

"Do I have to sip it, Dad?" said Al.

"Sip it to the rim," said Dad.

"Pack it in his back pack," said the gal to Dad.

Dad can pack it in the bag. Dad can fit the back pack in to the van.

The gal can pack Al in his van. Al can sit in the back. The gal can pat Al. Al can pat the gal.

Teacher/Parent Pages

Use the following questions to stimulate language growth, imagination, conceptual relationships, and higher-level thinking skills. These activities will encourage conversation and help develop language skills. Students must know that their ideas are important and that their questions will be heard. Have fun and accept all reasonable answers while praising and encouraging questioning from the students.

Vocabulary Expansion

Describe and define these words and phrases:

accident	doctor	medicine
hospital	release papers	medication
recuperate	document	visit
cheer up	forms	wheelchair
nurse	catnap	fond farewell

Language Expansion Activities

1. Pretend that you are in the hospital. Have your friends come in and cheer you up. What kinds of things would you say to cheer someone up?

2. Color a picture or make a gift for someone who is in the hospital or in a nursing home. Tell about what you have made and ask your teacher or parents to help you get it to the sick person.

Language Expansion Questions

1. Where was Al?

2. Why is today so special for Al and his family?

3. Did Dad go to sleep right away? What did he do first?

4. What did the nurse bring in for Al to sip?

5. How did Al get to the car? Why did the nurse have to take him in a wheelchair? What did Al say to the nurse when he left the hospital?

6. How did Al feel about going home? How did his parents feel?

7. Do you think that Al's pals came to visit him once he was home? What did they say to him?

8. Have you ever known anyone who was in the hospital? How did the people in the hospital help that person? What did you say to that person after he or she got home?

9. Hospitals help people get well, but they can appear to be a little scary. What things do you like about hospitals? What things might scare you a little?

10. Some people go the hospital for physical therapy; occupational therapy; or speech, hearing, or language therapy. Have you ever received therapy?

NICK IS BACK

UNIT 6

Phonology Concepts

- Place value for encoding: **-ck** (represents /k/ at the end of one-syllable words)
- Sometimes spelling depends on whether a sound comes at the beginning, middle, or end of a word.
- When the /k/ sound comes at the end of a one-syllable word, the spelling is almost always **-ck.**
    - Exception: when Mac is an abbreviated name (**Macmillan**, **Macarthur**)

Vocabulary

back	Nick	Rick	*of*
kick	pack	sack	
Mack	pick	sick	
Mick	Rat Pack	tack	

NICK IS BACK

Story Summary:

Al has just returned from the hospital, and his friends have come over to see him. Their old pal, Nick, knocks at the door. Nick had moved away some time ago, but has moved back into the neighborhood. The pals are thrilled to see Nick again and to introduce him to Pat, the new girl on the block. They exchange greetings and talk about things that have happened in the neighborhood since Al has been gone. The friends talk about their favorite rock group, the Rat Pack. Al picks out a new tape recording of the group and plays it for everyone. They listen and chat.

Nick is at the mat. Nick is rad. Nick is a kick.

Dad said, "Nick! It is Nick! Al, Sam, Pat, Tam, Kim! Kids, Nick is back!"

"Nick! Nick!" said Sam. "Nick is back! It is a kick!"

"I have to sit a bit, Nick," said Al.

"Sit and rap to Al, Nick," said Sam.

"A cab hit Al," Sam said to Nick. "The cab hit him in the back."

"I had a bad back, Nick. I had a bad hip," said Al. "I am sick of it!"

"I can dig it, man," said Nick.

"The fat cat had a Big B," said Sam.

"The cat is rad, man," said Nick. "I can dig the fat cat!"

"Sis had a big win," said Tam.

"Sis ran to tag Kim!" Pat said.

"Nick, I am Pat. I am a pal of Al's."

Nick said, "Pat, I am Nick. I am Al's pal. I am back to run and rap. I am a fan of the Rat Pack."

"The Rat Pack is a big hit," said Pat. "Al has the CD. Sam, pick the Rat Pack CD."

"I can dig it, man," said Nick. "I am hip to the Rat Pack. I am hip to Al's pals." Nick is back.

Teacher/Parent Pages

Use the following questions to stimulate language growth, imagination, conceptual relationships, and higher-level thinking skills. These activities will encourage conversation and help develop language skills. Students must know that their ideas are important and that their questions will be heard. Have fun and accept all reasonable answers while praising and encouraging questioning from the students.

Vocabulary Expansion

Describe and define these words and phrases:

return	introduce	record
move back	reminisce	compact disc
thrill	listen	rock group
unexpected pleasure	chat	favorite
exchange greetings	tape recording	old friend

Language Expansion Activities

1. Together with your friends, write a play about a kid who moves back to the neighborhood and sees all of his old friends. Put on the play for your teacher and parents.

2. Ask your classroom teacher, music teacher, or parents if you can pretend you and your friends have a rock group. Sing songs or lip-sync to your favorite recording.

Language Expansion Questions

1. Why were all the pals at Al's house?

2. Who showed up unexpectedly?

3. What did the friends talk to Nick about? Can you remember what Sam and Tam told Nick about the fat cat? What else do you remember? Look back in the text to help you remember.

4. Who was the new kid on the block that Nick didn't know?

5. How did the kids feel about their old friend showing up?

6. How did Nick feel about moving back to the neighborhood?

7. Do you know anyone who had to move to a different town or neighborhood? How did it feel when that person moved away?

8. When someone moves away, how can you keep in touch with the person and tell him or her what is going on in your neighborhood?

9. The kids in this story really like rock and roll music. What kind of music do you like? Why? Do you have a favorite song? Can you sing it for your friends?

10. The pals were at Al's house talking and listening to music. What do you do when you go to your friends' homes?